Wise Publications
London / New York / Paris / Sydney / Copenhagen / Madrid

International Music Publications Limited
Southend Road, Woodford Green, Essex IG8 8HN, England

Distributors:

Music Sales Limited
8/9 Frith Street, London W1V 5TZ, England.
Music Sales Pty Limited
120 Rothschild Avenue, Rosebery, NSW2018, Australia.

Order No.AM936430
ISBN 0-7119-5697-9

Visit the Music Sales' Internet Music Shop at
http://www.musicsales.co.uk

International Music Publications Limited
Southend Road, Woodford Green, Essex IG8 8HN, England.
International Music Publications Limited
25 Rue D'Hauteville, 75010 Paris, France.
International Music Publications Gmbh, Germany
Marstallstrasse 8, D-80539 Munchen.

Order Ref. 3821A
ISBN 1-85909-356-6

Music arranged by Roger Day
Music processed by Paul Ewers Music Design

Printed in the United Kingdom by
J.B. Offset Printers (Marks Tey) Limited, Marks Tey, Essex.

The Power Of Love ... 6

Misled ... 12

Think Twice ... 17

Only One Road ... 22

Everybody's Talkin' My Baby Down ... 28

Next Plane Out ... 34

Real Emotion ... 40

When I Fall In Love ... 46

Love Doesn't Ask Why ... 50

Refuse To Dance ... 55

I Remember L.A. ... 60

No Living Without Loving You ... 65

Lovin' Proof ... 70

Just Walk Away ... 76

The Colour Of My Love ... 82

Unison ... 87

The Last To Know ... 92

THE POWER OF LOVE

Words & Music by C.deRouge, G.Mende, J.Rush & S.Applegate.

1. The whis-pers in the morn-ing
(Verse 2 see block lyric)
of lov-ers sleep-ing tight,
are roll-ing by like thun-der now

as I look in your eyes.

I hold on to your bo - dy,

and feel each move you make,

your voice is warm and ten - der, a love that

The sound of your heart beat - ing ___ made it clear ___ sud-den-ly, the feel-ing that I can't go ___ on ___ is light years a-way. ___ 'Cause I'm your la -

D.%. al Coda

⊕ *Coda*

The pow - er of love, ___

Verse 2:
Lost is how I'm feeling
Lying in your arms,
When the world outside's too much to take,
That all ends when I'm with you.
Even though there may be times
It seems I'm far away,
Never wonder where I am
'Cause I am always by your side.

Misled

Words & Music by Peter Zizzo & Jimmy Bralower.

1. I thought I knew you, thought_ that I knew you well, we had a rhy-thm but_
(Verse 2 see block lyric)

se - ri - ous - ly___ mis - led.

Just a page in my his -

- to - ry,

just___ an - oth - er one of those mys - te - ries,

Verse 2:
Loving somebody
Ain't your average nine to five.
It takes conviction,
It takes a will to survive.
I'm not somebody
Who commits the crime and leaves the scene,
But when I've been dissed
I don't spend much time
On what might've been.

I'm not about self-pity
Your love did me wrong
Now I'm moving,
Moving on.

Verse 3: (D.𝄋.)
I'm not about self pity
Your love did me wrong
So I'm moving,
Moving on.

THINK TWICE

Words & Music by Andy Hill & Pete Sinfield.

1. Don't think I can't feel that there's some-thing wrong,—
(Verse 2 see block lyric)

you've been the sweet-est part— of my life for so long.

Verse 2:
Baby think twice, for the sake of our love
For the memory,
For the fire and the faith
That was you and me.
Babe I know it ain't easy
When your soul cries out for higher ground,
'Cause when you're halfway up
You're always halfway down.

But baby this is serious
Are you thinking 'bout you or us?

ONLY ONE ROAD

Words & Music by Peter Zizzo.

1. I'm look-ing back through the
(Verses 2 & 3 see block lyric)

years down this high-way._____ me-mo-ries, they all lead up to

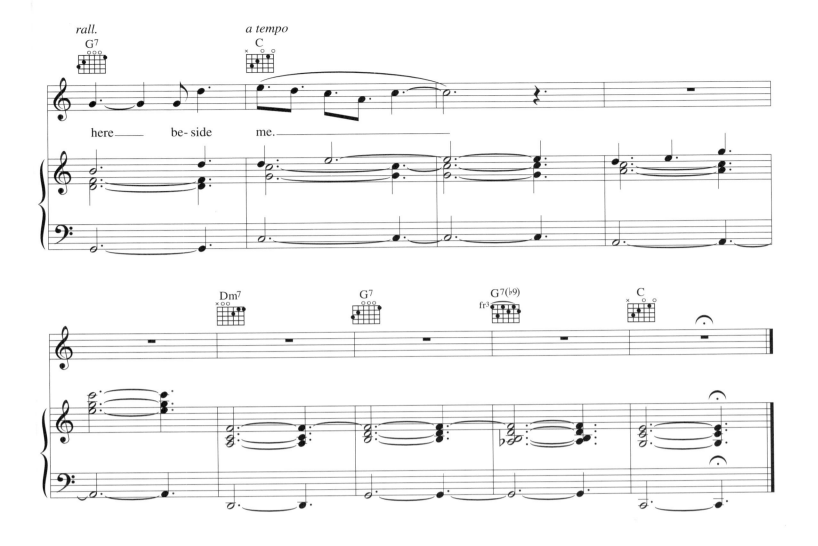

here_____ be-side me._____

Verse 2:
Here I stand, face to face
With this heart of mine
Living without you
I only fall behind.
We had a love most people never find
All this time I never realised
And the courage I finally found
Has made me turn around.

Verse 3:
I can still hear the song
Of your laughter,
I can still taste the sorrow
Of your tears
We said goodbye but our hearts did not hear
Now my love there's nothing left to fear.
With all my heart put me through
It leads me back to you.

Everybody's Talkin' My Baby Down

Words & Music by Russ De Salvo & Arnie Roman.

ev - 'ry - bo - dy's   talk - in' my___ ba - by down.___

Repeat vocals ad lib. to fade

Verse 2:
He's not like the others,
Nobody wants to see it,
They don't even want to try.
Judge a book by its cover
And you'll never know the story,
There's so much more than meets the eye.
Oh and I know his heart is true,
I don't need anyone to tell me what to do.

Next Plane Out

Words & Music by Diane Warren.

1. I lis- ten to the sound of the rain fall-ing down my win-dow, pray-in' for a
(Verse 2 see block lyric)

gen- tle wind_____ to bring my ba- by back a- gain.

Tryin' to be strong but I'm not get- ting a- ny strong- er; lone- li-

sleep at night_____ till he's sleep-in' here____ be-side____ me,____

_____ here be-side_____ me,____ it's

been too long____ since I held him in____ my____ arms,____ then I just won't____

_____ sleep at night,____ till he's sleep-in' here____ be-side____ me,____

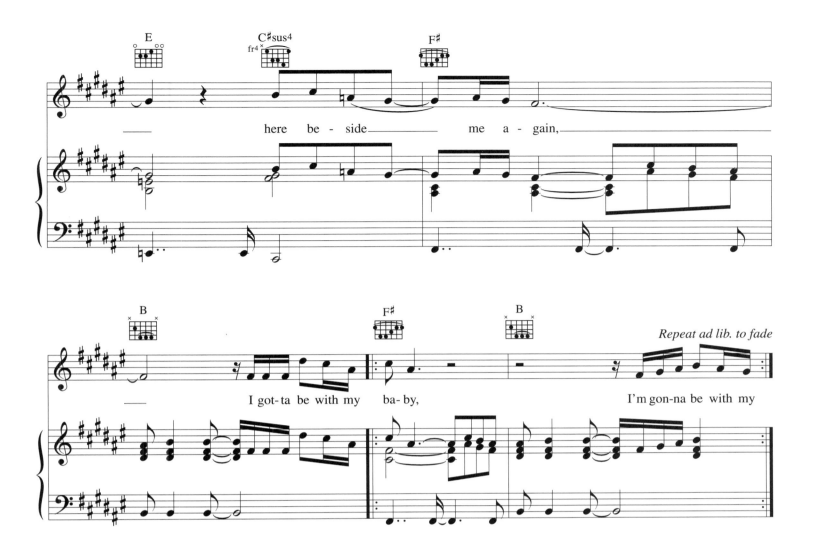

Verse 2:
Talkin' on the phone but that don't make it any better
Nothing's gonna ease this pain until I'm in his arms again.
Runnin' down the stairs, there's a taxi that's waiting for me
Loneliness, I'm gonna leave you far behind.

I'd walk for days through pouring rain, anything to be with him.
It's been too long, I can't be strong no more.

Additional lyrics to fade:
Gonna take the next plane or the next train
Gotta get there, gotta see my baby.
And nothing's gonna stop me from leaving this time.
Leavin' on the next plane out…

REAL EMOTION

Words & Music by Diane Warren.

You don't have to give me rings on my fin-gers, pro-mise me the moon and stars in the sky,____ or bring me ro-ses just to

show me you love—— me, that ain't gon - na win this heart—— of mine.

All the dia - monds you can buy won't im - press—— me,
(Verse 2 see block lyric)

pret - ty words ain't gon - na prove your love.—— I need more than just to - kens

of af - fec - tion, I'm not ask - ing for too much—— now ba - by,——

Verse 2:

Show me something that my heart can believe in
Imitation love don't mean a thing
Baby it's got to be the real thing or nothing
Show me what it's gonna be now baby.
I'm not asking much from you
Just a love that's deep and true, yeah…

WHEN I FALL IN LOVE

Music by Victor Young. Words by Edward Heyman.

mo - ment   I can feel that   you feel that   way   too,_____

is when I fall   in love   with   you._____

Coda

sun.   When I give   my   heart

it will be   com - plete - ly,   or I'll nev - er   give   my

LOVE DOESN'T ASK WHY

Words & Music by Philip Galdston, Barry Mann & Cynthia Weil.

Love does-n't ask why, _____ it speaks from the heart _____

and nev-er ex-plains. _____ Don't you know _____ that

Verse 2:
Now I can feel what you're afraid to say,
If you give your soul to me.
Will you give too much away,
But we can't let this moment pass us by.
Can't question this chance
Or expect any answers.
We can try,
Maybe we can try.

REFUSE TO DANCE

Words & Music by Charlie Dore & Danny Schogger.

Verse 2:
You said you're such a pretty thing,
You could make a mark.
I'll teach you all the steps you'll need,
Guide you through the dark.
Suddenly I thought I knew the song
The orchestra was playing.

I Remember L.A.

Words & Music by Tony Colton & Richard Wold.

seems a life - time a - go.

We were stars on Sun - set Bou - le - vard.

What a mo - vie we made.

There were days
(Verse 2 see block lyric)
in the sun———

that have stayed——— for - ev - er———

young.

Nights when pas - sion was in -

vin - ci - ble.———

We thought love——— would nev - er

Verse 2:
I remember goodbye,
I watched your plane out of sight.
Love was over, time to close the book,
Still I go back for one last look.

No Living Without Loving You

Words & Music by Diane Warren.

1. If you ev - er__ ev - er leave__ me,
(Verse 2 see block lyric)

life will go on stars will still be bright as dia - monds__ in the sky now,

Verse 2:
If you ever walk out this door,
What would I have left to live for?
What would there be left to do now,
What would I be without you now?
Oh, the clock wouldn't stop, no
Each day would go on just the same.
It wouldn't stop the sun and rain
But baby there would be…

LOVIN' PROOF

Words & Music by Diane Warren.

1. I know some lo - vers would be sa - tis - fied, with sweet 'I love yous' and some
(Verse 2 see block lyric)

Verse 2:
And if the love you got is strong and true
And if you love me like you say you do.
Your tender touch will tell the honest truth
And your kiss could never tell a lie.
'Cause I'd see it in your eyes,
There's one way to ease and doubt,
I tell you now.

JUST WALK AWAY

Words & Music by Albert Hammond & Marti Sharron.

Verse 2:
There'll never be a moment I'll regret,
I've loved you since the day we met.
For all the love you gave and all the love we made
I know I've got to find the strength to say

The Colour Of My Love

Words & Music by David Foster & Arthur Janov.

hold each oth - er___ oh so___ tight. I'll paint a

sun to warm your heart, swear - ing that we'll nev - er part,___

that's the co - lour of___ my love. I'll paint the

truth, show how I feel, try to make you com - plete - ly real,___ I'll use a

brush so light and fine to draw you close— and make you mine.

I'll paint a sun to warm your heart, swear-ing that we

nev - er ev - er part, that's the co - lour of_____ my_____

love. I'll draw the years all pass-ing by, so much to

Unison

Words & Music by Andy Goldmark & Bruce Roberts.

Ooh.

Some-where to - night

Verse 2:
Gleam of an eye, flash of a smile
Never too shy, playin' ever so wild.
Here we are, I'm relying on no one else,
But you and I we've come so far
No one else could ever steal away,
What we confide, who wants to know?

The Last To Know

Words & Music by Philip Galdston & Brock Walsh.

Verse 2:
You know how old friends will talk
A secret's hard to keep.
But this girl she says you're seeing
Sure sounds a lot like me.
Still it's not for me to say
If what I heard was true.
And I won't let myself believe a word
Till I hear it from you.